1935

read a good book, you need
either a lot of money or a library card.
Cheap paperbacks were available, but their
poor production generally mirrored the quality
between the covers. One weekend that year,
Allen Lane, Managing Director of The Bodley Head,
having spent the weekend visiting Agatha Christie,
found himself on a platform at Exeter station trying to
find something to read for his journey back to London.
He was appalled by the quality of the material he had to
choose from. Everything that Allen Lane achieved from that
day until his death in 1970 was based on a passionate belief
in the existence of 'a vast reading public for *intelligent*
books at a low price'. The result of his momentous vision
was the birth not only of Penguin, but of the 'paperback
revolution'. Quality writing became available for the price of
a packet of cigarettes, literature became a mass medium
for the first time, a nation of book-borrowers became a
nation of book-buyers – and the very concept of book
publishing was changed for ever. Those founding
principles – of quality and value, with an overarching
belief in the fundamental importance of reading –
have guided everything the company has
done since 1935. Sir Allen Lane's
pioneering spirit is still very much alive
at Penguin in 2005. Here's to
the next 70 years!

MORE THAN A BUSINESS

'We decided it was time to end the almost customary half-hearted manner in which cheap editions were produced – as though the only people who could possibly want cheap editions must belong to a lower order of intelligence. We, however, believed in the existence in this country of a vast reading public for intelligent books at a low price, and staked everything on it'
Sir Allen Lane, 1902–1970

'The Penguin Books are splendid value for sixpence, so splendid that if other publishers had any sense they would combine against them and suppress them'
George Orwell

'More than a business … a national cultural asset'
Guardian

'When you look at the whole Penguin achievement you know that it constitutes, in action, one of the more democratic successes of our recent social history'
Richard Hoggart

Where I Was

JAMES KELMAN

PENGUIN BOOKS

PENGUIN BOOKS

Published by the Penguin Group
Penguin Books Ltd, 80 Strand, London WC2R 0RL, England
Penguin Group (USA) Inc., 375 Hudson Street, New York, New York 10014, USA
Penguin Group (Canada), 10 Alcorn Avenue, Toronto, Ontario, Canada M4V 3B2
(a division of Pearson Penguin Canada Inc.)
Penguin Ireland, 25 St Stephen's Green, Dublin 2, Ireland
(a division of Penguin Books Ltd)
Penguin Group (Australia), 250 Camberwell Road, Camberwell, Victoria 3124,
Australia (a division of Pearson Australia Group Pty Ltd)
Penguin Books India Pvt Ltd, 11 Community Centre,
Panchsheel Park, New Delhi – 110 017, India
Penguin Group (NZ), cnr Airborne and Rosedale Roads, Albany,
Auckland 1310, New Zealand (a division of Pearson New Zealand Ltd)
Penguin Books (South Africa) (Pty) Ltd, 24 Sturdee Avenue,
Rosebank 2196, South Africa

Penguin Books Ltd, Registered Offices: 80 Strand, London WC2R 0RL, England

www.penguin.com

Stories first collected in *Lean Tales* by Jonathan Cape Ltd. 1985
This selection published as a Pocket Penguin 2005

1

Set in 11/13pt Monotype Dante
Typeset by Palimpsest Book Production Limited
Polmont, Stirlingshire
Printed in England by Clays Ltd, St Ives plc

Contents

Busted Scotch

I had been looking forward to this Friday night for a while. The first wage from the first job in England. The work-mates had assured me they played Brag in this club's casino. It would start when the cabaret ended. Packed full of bodies inside the main hall; rows and rows of men-only drinking pints of bitter and yelling at the strippers. One of the filler acts turned out to be a scotchman doing this harrylauder thing complete with kilt and trimmings. A terrible disgrace. Keep Right On To The End Of The Road he sang with four hundred and fifty males screaming Get Them Off Jock. Fine if I had been drunk and able to join in on the chants but as it was I was staying sober for the Brag ahead. Give the scotchman his due but – he stuck it out till the last and turning his back on them all he gave a big boo boopsidoo with the kilt pulled right up and flashing the Y-fronts. Big applause he got as well. The next act on was an Indian Squaw. Later I saw the side door into the casino section opening. I went through. Blackjack was the game until the cabaret finished. I sat down facing a girl of around my own age, she was wearing a black dress cut off the shoulders. Apart from me there were no other punters in the room.

Want to start, she asked.

Aye. Might as well. I took out my wages.

O, you're scotch. One of your countrymen was on stage tonight.

That a fact.

She nodded as she prepared to deal. She said, How much are you wanting to bet.

I shrugged. I pointed to the wages lying there on the edge of the baize.

All of it . . .

Aye. The lot.

She covered the bet after counting what I had. She dealt the cards.

Twist.

Bust . . .

the same is here again

My teeth are grut.

What has happened to all my dreams is what I would like to know. Presently I am a physical wreck. If by chance I scratch my head while strolling showers of dandruff reel onto the paved walkway, also hairs of varying length. Tooth decay. I am feart to look into a mirror. I had forgotten about them, my molars; these wee discoloured bones jutting out my gums and lonely, neglected, fighting amongst themselves for each particle of grub I have yet to pick. Jesus. And my feet – and this mayhap is the worst of my plight – my feet stink. The knees blue the hands filthy the nails grimy, uneatable. What I must do is bathe very soon.

One certainty: until recently I was living a life; this life is gone, tossed away in the passing. I am washed up. The sickness burbles about in my gut. A pure, physical reaction at last. I feel it heaving down there, set to erupt – or maybe just to remain, gagging.

It is all a mystery as usual. I am very much afraid I am going off my head. I lie on pavements clawing at myself with this pleasant smile probably on the countenance. I have been this way for years. More than half my life

3

to present has been spent in acquiring things I promptly dispose of. I seldom win at things. It is most odd. Especially my lack of interest. But for the smile, its well-being, the way I seem to regard people. It makes me kind of angry. I am unsure about much. Jesus christ.

Where am I again. London's the truth though I was reared in Glasgow. In regard to environment: I had plenty. But.

The weather. The hardtopped hardbacked bench concreted to the concrete patch amidst the grass. My spine against the hardback. My feet stuck out and crossed about the ankles. My testicles tucked between my thighs. I am always amazed that no damage is done them. I have forgotten what has happened to the chopper. The chopper is upright though far from erect. It lies against the fly of my breeks. And now uncomfortable.

Explanations sicken me. The depression is too real. A perpetual thirst but not for alcohol. Milk I drink when I find it. Smoking is bad. Maybe I am simply ill. Burping and farting. All sorts of wind. I should have a good meal of stuff. But even the thought. Jesus.

My hand has been bleeding. I cut it while entering a car. A stereo and one Johnny Cash cassette. My life is haunted by country & western music.

I have no cigarette in my gub.

And yet this late autumnal daylight. The spring in my step. Grinning all the while and wishing for hats to doff to elderly women. I am crying good-evening to folk. I might be in the mood for a game of something. Or a cold shower. When I settle down to consider a future my immediate straits are obliged to be conducive. I am grateful for the clement weather. Facts are to be faced. I am older than I was recently. And I was feart to show my face that same recently. Breakfast is an awful meal. If you dont get your breakfast that's you fucked for the day.

I cannot eat a Johnny Cash cassette.

Breakfast has always been the one meal I like to think I insist upon. When I have money I eat fine breakfasts. One of the best I ever had was right here in the heart of old London Town. A long time ago. So good I had to leave a slice of toast for appearances' sake. I was never a non-eater. Could always devour huge quantities of the stuff. Anything at all; greasy fried bread, burnt custard or eggs. Even with the flu or bad hangovers. A plate of soup at 4 in the morning. I cannot understand people scoffing at snails' feet and octopi although to be honest I once lifted a can of peasbrose from a supermarket shelf only to discover I couldnt stomach the bastarn stuff. So: there we are. And also food-poisoning I suppose. If I ever get food-poisoning I would probably not feel like eating. Apart from this

But not now. Not presently, and this is odd. My belly may have a form of cramp.

Immediately my possessions include money I shall invest in certain essentials as well as the washing of that pair of items which constitute the whole of my wardrobe in the department of feet viz my socks. For my apparel excludes pants and vest. An effect of this was my chopper getting itself caught in the zipping-up process that follows upon the act of pissing. Normally one is prepared for avoiding such occurrences. But this time, being up an alley off one of her majesty's thoroughfares, I was obliged to rush. ZZZIPPP. Jesus. The belly. Even the remembrance. For a couple of moments I performed deep breathing exercises aware that my next act would of necessity be rapid. And this was inducing vague associations of coronary attacks. My whole trunk then became icy cold. UUUNZZZIPP. Freed. It would not have happened had I been wearing pants. If I was being cared for pants would pose no problem, and neither would vests. Vests catch and soak up sweat unless they are made of nylon. In which case the sweat dribbles down your sides and is most damp and irritating.

My face looks to be ageing but is fine. A cheery face. It laughs at me from shop windows. The hairs protruding from my nostrils can be mistaken for the top of my moustache. The actual flesh, the cheekbones and red-veined eyeballs, the black patches round the sockets. Every single thing is fine. I am delighted with the lines. On my left – the right in fact, side of my nose has formed a large yellow head which I squeezed till the matter burst forth. I am still squeezing it because it lives. While squeezing it I am aware of how thin my skin is.

I put myself in mind of an undernourished 87 year old. But the skin surrounding the human frame weighs a mere 6 ounces. Although opposed to that is the alsatian dog which leapt up and grabbed my arm; its teeth punctured the sleeve of the garment I was wearing but damage to the flesh was nil.

I bathed recently; for a time I lay steeping in the grime, wondering how I would manage out, without this grime returning to the pores in my skin. The method I employed was this: I arose in the standing position. The grime showed on the hairs of my legs though and I had to rinse those legs with cold because the hot had finished. I washed my socks on that occasion. They are of good quality. I sometimes keep them stuffed in the back pockets of my jeans.

The present is to be followed by nothing of account. Last night was terrible. All must now be faced. It has much to do with verges and watersheds.

Taxis to Blackfriars Bridge for the throwing of oneself off of are out of the question.

I have the shivers.

Reddish-blue blisters have appeared on the soles of my feet. They are no longer bouncing along. I can foresee. Nothing of account will follow. For some time now the futility of certain practices has not been lost on me. I shall sleep with the shivers, the jeans and the

jumper, the socks and the corduroy shoes. I can forecast point A or point B: either is familiar. All will
depend on X the unknown (which also affords of an
either/or). The A and B of X equals the A and B that
follow from themselves, not A and not B being unequal
to not B and A. And they cannot be crossed as in Yankee
Bets. Yet it always has been this way and I alone have
the combinations.

I was planning on the park tonight. I left a brown paper
bag concealed in a hedge near the Serpentine for the
purpose. It will have been appropriated by now.

The trouble might well be sleep. I had a long one
recently and it may well have upset the entire bodily
functioning. This belly of mine. I must have slept for
10 hours. Normally I meet forenoons relatively alert.

Sheltering in an alley the other night, the early hours, in
a motionless state. I should have been smoking, had just
realized the cigarette in my gub as not burning where it
should have been burning. As I reached for a match I
heard movement. Two cats were on the job less than 20
yards distant. The alley banked by high walls. The cats
should have been free from spectators and yet here was
me, jesus. In a film I saw recently there was this scruffy
dog and a lady dog and he took her out for the night
down this back alley to meet his friends and these friends
of his were Chefs in an Italian Restaurant, one of whom
was named Luigi if I remember correctly. He brought
out a table and candlesticks and while the dogs sat down

the other friend came out with an enormous quantity of spaghetti and stuff. While they were tucking in out came Luigi again with a stringed instrument and him and his pal began singing an operatic duet.

This grass grows in a rough patch and cannot have it easy. The blades are grey green and light green; others are yellow but they lie directly on the earth, right on the soil. My feet were there and the insects crawled all around. A fine place for games. They go darting through the green blades and are never really satisfied till hitting the yellow ones below. And they dart headlong, set to collide all the time into each other but no, that last-minute body swerve. And that last-minute body swerve appears to unnerve them so that they begin rushing about in circles or halting entirely for an approximate moment.

I have to clear my head. I need peace peace peace. No thoughts. Nothing. Nothing at all.

Here I am as expected. The shoulders drooping; they have been strained recently. Arms hanging, and the fingers. Here: and rubbing my eyes to open them on the same again. Here, the same is here again. What else.

Manufactured in Paris

Whole days you spend walking about the dump looking for one and all you get's sore feet. I'm fucking sick of it. Sweaty bastarn feet. I went about without socks for a spell and the sweat was worse, streams in my shoes. Shoes! no point calling them shoes. Seen better efforts on a – christ knows what. Cant make you a pair of shoes these days. More comfort walking about in a pair of mailbags. A while ago I was passing a piece of waste ground where a few guys were kicking a ball about. On I went. We got a game going. Not a bad game. I kicked the stuffing out my shoes but. The seams split. Everybastarnthing split. Cutting back down the road with the soles flapping and that. And I had no spare pairs either by christ nothing, nothing at all. Then I found a pair of boots next to a pillarbox. This pair of boots had been Manufactured in Paris. Paris by christ. They lasted me for months too. Felt like they were mine from the start. I had been trying to pawn a suit that day. No cunt would take it. We dont take clothes these days is what they all said. Tramped all over the dump. Nothing. Not a bad suit as well. This is a funny thing about London. Glasgow – Glasgow is getting as bad right enough. They still take clothes but the price they give you's pathetic. I once spent forty-eight quid on a suit and when I took it along they offered me three for it. Three quid. Less than four months old by christ. A fine suit too, 14 ounce cloth and cut to my own specifications. The trimmings. That suit had the lot. I always liked suits. Used to spend a fortune on the bastards. Foolish. I gave it all up. It was a heatwave then as well right enough but an honest decision nevertheless.

Getting there

I stayed with the lorry and bypassed the dump. Down the A74 the driver was turning off into the weird Leadhills so I got out. I remained on this side of the road. A van. The driver wasnt going far, not beyond Lockerbie. I went. I spotted an inn in the distance and told him to stop, I felt like a couple of pints. Four customers including myself. Moving to a table within earshot I tried to concentrate on what they were saying but difficult to make heads or tails of, not just the accents.

I still had money. I had enough to rent some accommodation in the inn for the night and get rid of the beard and the grime and the old skin before returning up the road.

The man refused me a room. Full up. I was really surprised. I had expected a refusal of course but at the same time hadnt. He said the rooms were all taken. Aye. May his teeth fall out and his hair recede the bastard, saying the rooms were all taken yet allowing me to stay drinking his beer. I was being sociable, a bit sorry for them, not wanting to hurt their feelings by leaving too early for christ sake. Enough. I had to vanish in England. And I didnt have to walk. I had enough for a fucking bus. Or a train maybe. But the lift came almost at once and soon I was crossing the border.

The Appleton Arms. Pint of bitter and a pastie with

mustard. A husband and wife behind the bar: no bother the bed and breakfast sir. The outside lavatory with an ancient bicycle parked against the washbasin. Upstairs to immerse for twenty minutes in the grime and old skin then out for a smooth shave, and then back into the bath again till finally emerging in the pink. The desire for newly suiting, never seen nor heard of, outside of books by bad authors; the freshly pressed lined underwear and silk pyjamas, the valet to disrobe one, the smoking jacket velvet Jackson yes, hock'll do ably with the old cheese & water biscuits and invitations to the chambermaid.

The bed was soft, sagging in the centre, but I slept amazing and woke in fine fettle, in plenty of time for breakfast which was sadly meagre but good cups of dark red tea with plenty of toast to atone.

Waiting halfway up the sliproad onto the M6 I allowed three lifts to go by, attempting to explain that it had to be London or bust. Springtime in old King's Cross. But I could see the drivers' faces tightening into huffs. I feel bad about that, three probables vanishing from the paths of other wayfarers.

Then the rain of course.

So aye, Bristol? Aye, yes, Bristol's fine mate. Maybe the M4 or something.

Very snug inside the big artic, the driver's cassette blasting it out and no need to gab but just enjoy the ride down the safe inside lane, the drone of the windscreen-wipers while the rain, battering hard down on the cabin roof.

Fuck the M4. I liked Bristol on sight. Something about

the place. Yet I couldnt remember having passed through before. As though last time along I maybe missed it. But I had been heading northwest, detouring via Wales and according to maps the passing through Bristol is inevitable. That's a strange thing.

Windswept Weymouth and nothing to add except I still had money.

A bad time aboard. Pounding waves. Passengers having to heave out their guts here there and everywhere; the mess on the saloon floor, it streaming about, the bits of meat and veg amongst the Guinness-type froth but the grumpy barman stood me a pint when he saw I wasnt getting affected. I told him a yarn about working on the boats off Cromarty – in fact it must have been down to the time spent plying the Glasgow buses over cobbled streets, those boneshaking old efforts probably ensuring I can never be seasick again. And so pleased with myself I would have ordered a three-course meal if the cash had stretched.

. . .

An old guy had been tethering a group of rowing boats, down on the beach, to the side of a wee pier; then he sat on a deckchair up by a green hut which was advertising fishing tackle for hire. Going over to him and saying: I want your job ya old bastard.

. . .

This island. And so long to accept the warmer weather as a fact. It bringing out a great many people, all young-looking for some reason maybe to do with the summer looming ahead. The jeans and T-shirts and sandals or trainers. Even on the concrete promenade my feet are comfortable.

The clouds are not in sight.

In a delicatessen I could buy 2 ounces of cold spiced sausage and rolls. Narrow streets and pavements and all of the tiny shops. The promenade is very long and straight. Word of an old castle. The rest of it to be explored. In a pub later on I was sitting at the bar, eaves-dropping on the chat of three girls who were sipping at blackcurrant & Pernod; and the sensation of being offered the opportunity. I could have explained the present predicament. But there was nothing to be said then till finally it was too too late, and it was getting dark, the rain probably drizzling. Staying in the bar, my back to the wall – yet still content – the feet outstretched beneath the table and tucking them under when some-one walked by, with apologies articulated that I might be reasonably understood; clearing the accent to please, in other words: in a good way but.

The barmaid roused me. It had to be around 11.30 p.m.

I knew all about the police here. Throw you off the place at the slightest excuse – unfixed abodes the espe-cial cause. Twice in ten minutes I had to go down an alley to piss. Yet I still wasnt too worried, it was so very dark, so very quiet, and neither strollers nor stray animals. A patrol car rolled by. I had the smoke cupped in the palm of my right hand.

Now the rain.

Out onto the promenade I cut smartly across, down the stone steps to the sands immediately below the big wall; right along quickly, to the farthest point, and up, retracking to the third last shelter. I had to take this chance I think though well aware it was obvious, unsafe. I sat on the bench in the side exposed to the Sea, elbows on knees and hands propping up the head. The rain belting down, like a storm, the incredible noise. I was probably trying to sort things out about the dump and being here instead but I dont remember doing any of that at all, just entering a kind of daze, a kind of numbness, literally, having to get up and hop about to regain sensation proper. And the rain blowing in, having to huddle into the side of the wall, escaping the wind but the draughts, the draughts were just not, they were too much – not too much, they were just, they were like the wind, sudden blasts. And this strange experience of hearing a clock strike. I had no idea of time, I had sixteen pence in my pocket. Then later, later on, through the blackest greys a little bit of red showed in snatches; enough for the luck to be hitting on. I knew it. A certainty. No need to hop.

. . .

The tide was out. I walked the sands a furlong or so, the boots squeaking then squelching. Sand worms. Red veins. So so tiny, thin. The first time I ever saw them though I had often looked at the mound of twirls they left dotted about. Amazing. What are they like at all, the red things. And sitting on my heels gazing back to the promenade, the row of villas, guest-houses and hotels. And back at the Sea, two boats an inch apart on the horizon.

The City Slicker and The Barmaid

I came to someplace a few miles south of the Welsh border and with luck managed to rent a tent on a farm. Not a camping site. I was the one mug living on the dump and could only stay on condition I completed certain set tasks such as painting barn walls or driving tractors. And whenever the farmer was away on business I had to guide his ramshackle lorry into the village.

I also received cash for these tasks.

The grass was long in the field where I had to pitch the tent. Closeby was a barn. Here big rats jumped about getting fat on the hay and feed stored inside. Sometimes I discovered paw marks on the grease in my frying pan. This proves the rats got into my tent though the farmer would never believe me. During the night I liked to sit at the top end with a bottle in my hand waiting for a thing to creep in. And the hedge surrounding this field was full of beetles and other flying insects. When I lit my candle they broke into the tent, perched on the roof till I was sleeping, then came zooming down on me, eating my blood and knocking their knees in my hair. I was always waking in the middle of the night scratching and clawing at my skalp.

The actual farm animals themselves did not worry me. Although after sundown a pack of cows used to try and sniff me; they came wastling along at my back without a sound bar the shshsh of their smelly tails. And no comfort entering the tent with my boots soaked through with dew. I was obliged to take them off at the door, seated on the groundsheet with the tent flaps wide open. A terrible tent. Two inch walls and sagging everywhere. The kind of effort a scoutmaster buys at christmas for his six years old son. And the ground-sheet was always covered in clumps of grass, earwigs and spiders. Dung too at times when I had thought my boots okay enough to walk straight in.

No sleeping bag. Terrible itchy exarmy blankets hired from the farmer's wife at 30 pence a week. Of course my feet stuck out at the bottom and I can never sleep wearing socks.

The farmhands were continually cracking jokes in Oi Bee accents at my expense. Sometimes I would laugh, or stare – other times I replied in aggressive accents of my own which got me nowhere since they pretended not to understand what I was saying. Because I drove the lorry I was accorded a certain respect. In the local den of a pub I was known as Jock the Driver. The previous driver was an Irishman who worked seven years on the farm till one Saturday night he went out for a pish in the lavatory round the back of the pub. It was the last they ever saw of him. A man to admire. The men working beside me were yesmen to the core. Carried tales about each other to the farmer and even to me if the farmer was off on business. Whole days they spent gossiping. I never spoke to them unless I had to. The tightest bunch of bastards I have ever met. Never shared their grub or mugs of tea. Or their cash if you were skint. And they never offered you a cigarette. If you bought them a drink they thought you were off your head and also resented it because they felt obliged to buy you one back. In their opinion city folk were either thieves or simpletons. An amazing shower of crackpots the lot of them.

The barmaid in this pub was a daughter of the village. I think she must have hated me because I represented outside youth. And apart from myself there were no other single men of her age in the dump. She was chaste I think unless the Irishman ever got there which I doubt. I never fancied her in the first place. A bit tubby. Just that if I hadn't tried I thought the regulars might have felt insulted – the barmaid not good enough etcetera for a city slicker like me. The night I made the attempt was awful. It reminds me of B feature imitation Barbara Stanwyck films.

Once or twice the manager used to bolt his doors and allow a few regulars to stay behind after closing time. He must have forgotten about me. With the shutters drawn and the local constable in the middle of his second pint of cider I for some reason threw an arm about the barmaid's waist for which I was dealt an almighty clout on the jaw. What a fist she had on her. I was so amazed I tried to land her one back but missed and fell across the table where the constable was sitting, knocking the drink over him. I was ejected.

Long after midnight, maybe as late as two in the morning, I came back to apologize if anyone was still about, and also to collect the carry-out I had planked in the grass behind the lavatory. I had been wandering about retching for ages because of that country wine they had been feeding me. Powerful stuff. Inside the pub the lights had been dimmed but I knew they were there. I could hear music coming faintly from the lounge. I crept round the side of the building then up on my toes and peering in through the corner of the frosted glass I spied the barmaid there giving it a go as the stripper. Yes. Doing a strip show on top of the lounge bar watched by the copper, the manager and one or two regulars, including an unhealthy old guy called Albert Jenkinson who worked alongside me on the farm. And all silent while they watched. Not a smile amongst them. Even the drink was forgotten. Just the quick drag on the smoke.

I lost my temper at first then felt better, then again lost my temper and had to resist caving in the window and telling them to stick the countryside up their jacksie.

No one noticed me. I did not stay very long. Her body was far too dumpy for a stripper and her underwear was a bit old fashioned. Her father worked as a gardener in the local nursery and rarely went into the pub.

Once I got my wages the following week, and it was safe, I got off my mark and took the tent with me.

the paperbag

What was the point anyway, there didnt seem to be any at all. I footered about with the newspaper, no longer even pretending interest. It was useless. I felt totally useless – I was useless, totally. I crumpled the newspaper in both hands, watching it, seeing the shapes it made, the way its pages became.

I would go on a walk; that was what to do. I uncrumpled the newspaper and rolled it into a neat sort of bundle, to carry it in my right hand, and then began walking. O christ but it was good to be alive – really. Really and truly. I felt magnificent. Absolutely wonderful. What was it about this life that made a body feel so good, so absolutely fucking wonderful. Was everybody the same. Now I was chuckling. Not too loudly but, no point worrying folk. A woman approached, her message bags not too full, preoccupied, the slight smile on her face. Where else could it be? Her eyes. Her eyes could be smiling. Is that possible. I was chuckling again. And then the mongrel appeared. I recognized it right away: a stupid kind of beast, even how it trotted was a bit stupid – plus that something about it, that odd look it could give – as though it was a fucking mule! Mule. Why did I think of that, mule. Well it was a beast and it was stupid-looking – or rather, it behaved stupidly, the way it looked at folk and didnt do as they desired, they wanted it off the pavement out their road but it never went off the pavement out their road, it just carried on trotting till sometimes they even had to get out of its road. Amazing. Imagine giving it a kick! Just going up and giving it a kick. Or else poisoning it. Taking it away on a long walk and then dumping it – maybe on a bus journey right out the other side of the city, pushing it off and shutting the door, leaving the thing yelping in astonishment. What'll happen to me now! Christ sake the dirty bastard he's pushed me off the bus and shut the door and I dont know where I've landed!

Imagine being a dog but – murder! people taking you wherever they like and you dont have a say in the matter. Here boy, here boy. I would hate to be a dog like that, getting ordered about by cunts without knowing what for, not having a genuine say on the matter. Horrible, really fucking horrible. And then getting put down for christ sake sometimes for nothing, no reason, just for doing what dogs do. Biting people!

Crazy, walking along the road thinking about such stuff. Absolute fucking nonsense. Mongrels by christ! But that's what happens. And thinking of that is better than thinking of nothing. I would say so anyway. Or would I? The trouble with being useless is this thinking; it becomes routine, you cannot stop yourself. I think all the time, even when I'm reading my newspaper. And the things I think about are fucking crazy. Imagine going up to somebody and saying Hey, have you ever felt like screwing the queen? Just to actually say it to somebody. Incredible. This is the kind of thing I can think about. I cannot help it. I didnt always think like it either. I used to think about ordinary things. Or did I? I find it hard to tell.

Then she was coming towards me but I didnt notice properly till there we were having to get out each other's road. Sorry, I said and I smiled in a hopeful manner. I was lost in abstraction . . .

And then I smiled coyly, this coyliness compensating for the use of the long word, abstraction. But everything was fine, everything was fine, she understood. It's okay, she replied, I was a bit abstracted myself.

And of course she was! Otherwise she'd've fucking bumped into me if she hadnt been careful to get out my road while I was getting out of hers!

Then she had dropped a paperbag and was bending down to retrieve it; and once she had retrieved it she opened it and peered inside.

And so did I!

I just fucking stretched forwards and poked my head next to hers – not in any sort of ambiguous way but just to peer into the bag same as her. She glanced at me, quite surprised. Then we smiled at each other as though in appreciation of the absurdity of my reaction.

And yet it had been a true reaction. Normally I'm not a nosey person. But having said all of that I have to confess that it maybe was a bit ambiguous, maybe I was trying to get a bit closer to her because it should be said that she was nice, in fact she was really nice. The way she was standing there and then bending to get her paperbag etc., the smile she had, and above all that understanding, how she had eh o christ o christ, o christ and there wasnt anything I could say, nothing, nothing at all because I was without funds, absolutely fucking without funds. So after a wee moment I smiled, an unhealthy smile – even at the actual instant it was happening I was thinking how it would be to have a blunderbuss whose muzzle I could stick my head into and then pull the trigger.

It was a surprise to see her still standing there. How come she was still standing there the way things were. I didnt even know her. I had never seen her before in all my life. I said: Eh d'you live eh roundabout? But she didnt reply. She was frowning at something. She hadnt paid the slightest attention to what I had said. And no wonder, the things I say, they're always so fucking boring, so fucking boring. Why am I the most fucking boring bastard in the whole fucking world? Her cake was bashed. Inside the paperbag was a cake and it had become bashed because of falling on the pavement. I could have mentioned that to her. That was something to say, instead of this, this fucking standing, just fucking standing there, almost greeting, greeting my eyes out. I was just standing there having to stop myself greeting like a wean, looking at her, trying to make her see and by making her see stopping myself and making everything fine, everything fine, if she would just stay on a minute or two and we could maybe have a chat or something – just a couple of minutes' chat, that would have worked the oracle, maybe, to let her see. Because after all, she hadnt been put off by the way I had peered into her bag; she had recognized it as a plain ordinary reaction, the sort of thing that happens out of curiosity – a bit stupid right enough, the way a kid acts. And yet she hadnt been put off. Not even as a person had I put her off. She smiled at me, a true smile – there again, it had happened at the point of departure

for yes, that moment had indeed arrived and was gone now, gone forever. And so too was she, trotting along the pavement, away to a life that was much better than this one. If I could run after her and clasp her by the hand.

I had unrolled the newspaper and was glancing at the back page, an item of football news. I could just have run after her and said Sorry – for having almost bumped right into her and making her drop the paperbag. But what was the point of it all? it was useless, totally fuck-ing useless. I crumpled the newspaper in my right hand then grabbed it from there with my left, and continued the walk.

Where I was

At least I am elsewhere. A wind like the soundtrack of
a North Pole documentary rages underneath. I have
absconded from my former abode leaving neither note
nor arrears. I left arrears, I left no cash to discharge
them. No explanations of any kind. Simply: I am somewhere else. No persons who knew me then or in fact
at any time know of my whereabouts. Season: Mid-
winter. Equipage: To be listed, but boots as opposed to
other things I may have worn previously. And also a
leather pouch instead of my old tobacco tin. Jesus, and
also a piece of cloth resembling a tartan scarf.

There are no lights. I am resting having walked many
miles. I am well wrapped up; brown paper secured
round my chest by means of the scarf crossed and
tucked inside my trousers, a couple of safety pins are
in there somewhere too. My health has got to remain
fine otherwise my condition will deteriorate. At present I do not even have a runny nose. I stopped here
because of the view. No other reason, none, nothing. I
look down between mainland and island. Both masses
ending in sheer drops, glowering at each other, but
neither quite so high as where I am though maybe they
are. Miles separate us. How many, I would be guessing.
Rain pours. Sky very grey. The truth is I cannot tell what
colour the sky is. May not even be there for all I know.

26

And I reckon it must be past 10 o'clock. A car passed some time ago. A Ford it was but a big one. Expensive model.

Below, the tide reaches up to the head of the loch. No islets visible. My boots are not leaking. I laid out six quid on them. In the glen at the head of the loch are houses; I see lights there, and also opposite where I am a big house can be seen – white during daylight I imagine. A large dwelling house. It looks far from safe. Surrounded by tall, bent trees. A cabin cruiser tethered to a narrow jetty. Apart from all this nothing of moment.

Back a distance sheep were nibbling weeds. I saw them from thirty yards and knew what they were immediately.

I left the room in Glasgow recently and got here before the Ford car. There is something good about it all I cannot explain away. Not only the exhilarating gale blowing the dirty skalp clean. Nor the renunciation of all debts relating to the past while. Maybe it is as simple.

From here the road twists, falls, to a village where there has to be a pub. As pubs go it shall be averagely not bad. I wont stop. The place will be closed anyway. This afternoon I slept in a public convenience. Clean, rarely used by the smell of it. I should have invested in a tent. Not at all – a good thick waterproof sleeping-bag would have been sufficient. I am spending money as I go but have a deal of the stuff, enough to be without worries for some time. If I chance upon a rowing boat tied near the shore I may steal it and visit the island across the way. Unlikely. I could probably swim it. The gap is deceptive but perhaps no more than two miles.

Drowning. At one time it would have presented no problem. Never mind.

I enjoy this walking. Amble and race, set off at a trot, and once I ran pell-mell for quite a stretch – till a tractor saw me. Taking baby steps and giant steps, assume odd postures and if a car passes I shriek with laughter. Sing all songs. My jaw aches. My ears ache. Maybe the wind clogs them up. Noises in my head. Sounding like a lunatic. But my nose remains dry. Probably impending bronchitis. Next time I waken with a bone-dry throat I shall know for sure. When I become immune to the wind everything will be fine. Immune to the wind.

Well stocked up on tobacco, always carrying cheese and whisky in case of emergencies; fever and that. The notion of buying a pipe. I have no room for useless piles of tobacco. I handrolled pipe tobacco in the past. Terrible stuff.

From Ardanruiach the road curves steeply through a glen owned by someone whose name escapes me. Stiff climb. Tired my knees in particular. For the eventual relief of walking with straight legs I firstly walked with bent ones, at the knees. Black specs in front or slightly above my eyes. The blood cannot be as good as the best. But the wind. I heard it all the time. Loud racket never dying. I thought of climbing a mountain. The real problem is rain. Whenever it falls I am affected. Soaks in knocking my hearing out. I am unable to look up for any length of time. It is damaging my boots and perhaps my coat. If my hair is plastered down over my brow in too irritating a manner water will drip down my sleeve when I push it up. Terrible sensation. The vehicles splash me. The face red raw; my nose must be purple, the constant drip drip from either nostril. Beads hang onto my eyebrows, cling at my eyelashes, falling from my chin down my neck – from my hair at the back down my neck it streams down my spinal cord, gets rubbed and rubbed by my trouser waistband into the skin at the small of my back. And no respite for my hands inside the coat pockets. The sleeves of this coat are far too wide so only my flesh actually enters each pocket, the wet cloth irritating my wrists, and tiny pools of water gathering within the nylon material. The rain spoils the walk but it brightens. Always brightens eventually. Then I see water on the leaves of bushes and I can skite the branch of a tree to see the beads drop. The road dries in patches, swiftly, sometimes I can sit on such a spot though not for long of course.

In the future I hope to sleep during the day, regularly. Apparently some folk do sleep on their feet the bastards. And I try striding with my eyes shut once I have noted the direction.

I enjoy night. Not dusk so much because I know pubs do business; possibly it gets easier when the days lengthen. I shall sleep all day perhaps. With this constant exercise four hours' kip wont be enough. And I shall be swimming when the water heats. Eating does not worry me yet. My money will run out. My best sleep so far was had in a hostel closed for the winter. Very simple to enter. No food but plenty of firewood which burned fine. I spread all my clothes on the backs of chairs in front of it. And washed both pairs of socks. And had a complete body wash which might not have been a good idea since two or three layers of old skin went down the drain. This explains why I am freezing. Unfortunately I appear to be really particular about clean feet thus socks although I dont bother about underwear, seldom have any. Up until the wash I was wearing each pair on alternate days and both when sleeping. They had a stale, damp smell. My feet were never wholly dry. Small particles stuck to the toejoints, the soles. I had to see all this during the changing process. In future I may steel myself if warmer feet can be guaranteed. And may even take to wearing both pairs daily, in other words keep them on at all times. Christ I wont be surprised if I catch the flu. I have acted very foolishly. No wonder tramps wash rarely. Yet what happens when the summer comes and I want a swim.

I considered staying in the hostel indefinitely. I could also have erected a sign for other wayfarers explaining how easy it was to break and enter, but did not. The reason reflects badly on me.

This day was bitter. Never warm inside the coat. That fucking wind went through me. Tried everything from walking sideways to hiding behind trees. All I could finally do was stride along punching my boots hard down on the road with my shoulders rigid, hunched up. This induced prolonged shivering but was the best I could manage. Every part of me cold, sick cold. Now and then I stopped for a swig of the stuff.

When the road closed onto the water again I cut off through the marsh and down to the edge of the loch or maybe it was the sea. There was land far out. An island? Amazing silence. Nothing but the waves breaking, lapping in over the pebbles. Where I was the wind was forgotten. Almost warm. I took off the coat and used it as a cushion on a dry rock a little way back. No fishing boats. I saw only small birds, landbirds, the country equivalent to sparrows I suppose. My mind got into a certain state. The usual blankness. A trance or something like it. Time obviously passed. Clear. I finished my whisky and chain-smoked. Staying put. No wish to walk the shore in search of a better position. The rain came later. Fine drizzle, spotting the water. I watched on for a bit then had to put the coat across my shoulders and shelter beneath the trees. But I remained for quite a while and might have pitched a tent there.

In a betting shop to the rear of Shaftesbury Avenue

Heh John! John . . . I grinned: How you doing?

He made to walk past me.

John, I said quickly, how's it going – I thought you were in Manchester?

What . . . He looked at me. My name's no John. He sniffed and glanced sideways, then muttered: McKechnie.

McKechnie! Christ. Aye . . . I thought you were in Manchester? How you doing man?

He looked away from me. I've no been in Manchester for years. And again he made to walk past, but I stepped slightly to the front.

Christ, so you left!

Aye, years ago. He sniffed, gazed round the interior of the betting shop. It was a poky wee dump of a place and with nearly quarter of an hour till the first race only a couple of people were about. McKechnie looked at them. He was holding a rolled newspaper in his left hand.

So how long you been here then? you been here long?

What . . . naw. He glanced up at the board to where a clerk had gone to scribble the names of the day's nonrunners. He glanced across to the counter; the two women were eating sandwiches, sipping at cups of tea.

Then he glanced back to me, and he frowned momentarily. He said: Mind that wife of mine? I'm in for a divorce off her. She wants the wean, but I'm getting the wean. Lawyer says I'm a certainty. And these lawyers know the score . . .

Aye.

He nodded.

After a moment I said, Aye – these lawyers!

He nodded again. The door opened and in came a punter, then another. McKechnie had noticed them and he moved slightly. And then the knocking sound from the Extel speaker and through it came the first betting show of the day.

The other people were now standing gazing at the formpages tacked onto the walls; up at the board the clerk was marking in the prices against the listed runners, he held a fresh cigarette cupped in one hand.

McKechnie unrolled his newspaper.

So you left then?

What . . .

Manchester, you left?

He nodded without taking his gaze from the newspaper, not even raising his head. But he muttered, Aye – I went to Sheffield.

Sheffield!

Mmhh.

Christ sake!

At this point a further betting show came through. When it was over I said: Sheffield!

Mmm. He sniffed, still gazing at the racing page.

Did you never think of going back then? to

Manchester I mean – did you never think of going back?

What . . . He shook his head, and he grunted: Hard race this.

I shrugged. Favourite cant get beat, it's a good thing.

Aye . . . He indicated the selection of one of the racing journalists. That's what he says and all. I dont know but, I hate backing these fucking odds-on shots. It's one to beat it I want . . . And he glanced at me, and added: Warrior Chief's supposed to be the only danger . . .

Aye, it's got a wee chance right enough. Heh d'you ever see Tommy on your travels?

Tommy? His forehead wrinkled as he glanced at me again.

Tommy, christ, you must mind him – used to work in the building game. Carried the hod or something.

Aw aye, aye, I mind him. Subbied.

You're right! Hh! I laughed. That's right man – Tommy, christ: lucky bastard eh! must've made a real few quid, no having to pay any tax or fuck all.

McKechnie nodded; then he sniffed and indicated the comments on the race by the journalist. According to this cunt, Warrior Chief's the only danger.

Aye, it's got a chance. Heh, I wouldnt mind a start subbying somewhere myself, eh – that's the right way if . . .

Hard race but, McKechnie muttered, a lottery, fucking lottery.

Another betting show was in progress and I altered my stance a bit, to be able to see the racecard in his newspaper. Then when it was over I said: What about yourself man, you working?

Who me . . . He sniffed, he glanced up at the board, rolling up his newspaper at the same time. Hang on a minute, he said, I need a pish.

And he walked off immediately.

I went to the nearby wall; the front page of the *Chronicle* was tacked here and I read the post-mortems on yesterday's results. A couple of minutes before the *off* I looked up. I noticed McKechnie, he was standing right beside two old codgers who didnt look to have the price of a packet of Rizlas between them.

And it dawned on me: there wasnt any toilets in this fucking betting shop.

I crossed the floor. He had taken a brand new packet of cigarettes from his pocket and was unwrapping the cellophane. He looked at me and extended the packet. Ta, I said. When we were smoking I smiled: To tell you the truth man, I never even knew you were married never mind in for a divorce!

What! christ, where've you been? Married – I've been married for years.

Hh. Who to? that wee thing back in Manchester?

He glanced at me: I was well married before I hit that fucking place. He sniffed. She thinks she'll get the wean but she's got no chance.

Good . . . I nodded. But still and all, sometimes . . .

Hang on a minute, I'm just . . . He turned and squinted at the formpage on the wall. Then he was edging along to where another punter stood and I could hear him mutter, This Warrior Chief's supposed to have a chance of upsetting the favourite . . .

I stepped over and peered at the form. Could do, I said,

35

but the favourite's got a good bit of class about her. Won hell of a comfortably last time out and the way I heard it she won hell of a cleverly, a hands and heels game.

The punter was manoeuvring himself to write out his line in such a way that nobody would see what he wrote. Suddenly McKechnie thumped the page on the wall. That's the thing I'm feart of, he said.

Dark Lights?

Dark Lights. He nodded, and he grinned briefly. Dark Lights . . .

Hh.

Aye, he went on, they've just stuck it in here.

What?

Aye, fucking obvious.

I nodded. It's got a chance right enough. But you cant always rely on winning form out of *maiden* races; I mean this is the first time it'll have run in a *handicap*, and you know as well as . . .

Hang on a minute, he said. And he walked to a different wall, to where a youth was standing gazing at another formpage; I could see him begin muttering.

Then the runners were being loaded into the starting stalls and the youth strode to the counter to place his bet; and shortly afterwards McKechnie had scribbled down his own bet and was striding to the counter just as they were set to come under orders. And when the woman had returned him his change and receipt he went to the other side of the room.

It was no a bad night-life in Manchester, I said when I got there.

What . . .

The night-life – Manchester. Mind you, it's no bad here if you know where to go. Murder when you're skint but.

He nodded.

Aye, I said.

He sniffed: I've no been here that long.

What! christ, ach dont worry, dont worry man I mean you'll soon find your way about – once you get the hang of their fucking tube system. And then, when you've got a few quid you can always . . .

I'm going up the road the morrow.

Eh?

Edinburgh. I'm going to Edinburgh.

Edinburgh! Christ sake. Edinburgh . . . I nodded. Aw aye, I'll tell you . . .

OFF BRIGHTON: THEY'RE OFF BRIGHTON: RUNNING 2.17: AND ON THE OFF THEY BET FOUR TO NINE NUMBER THREE, FIVE TO TWO BAR . . .

The race was over the minimum trip and soon they were entering the final stretch; taking the lead at the distance the favourite won going away – exactly the style in which an odds-on shot should win.

A horse by the name of Lucy's Slipper ran on to snatch second place close home. Neither Warrior Chief nor Dark Lights had received a mention throughout the entire commentary.

But McKechnie was grinning all over his face. Told you, he shouted, I fucking told you – that favourite: couldnt get beat – a fucking certainty! I knew it.

I nodded. Trained at Epsom as well if you noticed. These Epsom runners usually do good here, the track, nice and sharp, fast. And . . .

The forecast! McKechnie was laughing and he elbowed me in the ribs: I've dug out the forecast!

What?

The forecast – I've dug it out, that Lucy's Slipper! a certainty for second place, I knew it, I fucking knew it.

Hh.

He winked. I'll tell you something: the shrewd money, all the shrewd money's down to it. Know what I mean? they've just stuck it in here – for the forecast. Fucking obvious. Think they're going to take odds-on on a single when they can lift five or six to one on a fucking forecast? you kidding!

Aye, eh.

Kept saying it all morning to myself: look for a forecast I says, look for a forecast, this favourite cant get beat, look for a forecast. McKechnie grinned and shook his head. And after a moment he glanced to the pay-out window. The youth stood there, holding a receipt in one hand. McKechnie walked across; he was still grinning; then I could hear him say: So you got it?

The youth nodded, and they began comparing notes on the following race in between congratulating each other on the last, as they waited for the *weigh-in*.

McKechnie copped the next three winners but the youth didnt return to the pay-out window. It had become difficult to tell where he was getting his selections; various people were going to the pay-out and McKechnie seemed to be in contact with most of them.

He kept edging his way in and out of places, eaves-dropping here and there. He had this peculiar kind of shuffle, dragging his heels as if his shoes were hell of a heavy – he probably kept a reserve fund stuffed inside his socks the bastard.

I went out for a breath of fresh air. I walked up and down the street a couple of times. Back inside he continued to dodge me but then I stepped right in front of him and said: A nicker, just a nicker, that's all, I'll give you it back man, honest.

Aw I cant, he said, no the now – I'm going to stick the lot on this next favourite. I'll weigh you in after but, dont worry, you'll be alright then – a nicker? Aye, no bother, you'll be alright for a nicker.

He about turned and walked to study a formpage, close in beside the two old codgers. Then just as the first show of betting came through on the next race I noticed him glance at me. Moments later he did a vanishing trick out the door. He probably thinks I didnt see him but I did.

A Nightboilerman's notes

The bunker faces outwards, away to the far corner of the ground surface area. When it requires replenishing (twice nightly) I push the bogey out into the corridor and through the rearmost swing doors, down the steep incline onto the pathway by the canal, along to where the coalmountains pile some thirty yards from the embankment. It is good to walk here, the buckled rattle of the bogey wheels only emphasizing the absence of noise. The Nightoutsideman has charge of this area. I used to envy him. His job has always seemed so straight-forward in comparison to this one of mine. He sits on his chair to the side of his hut door, gazing to the sky or to the canal. I walk past him but he doesnt look across, not until he hears that first strike of my shovel into the coal, when he turns and waves.

It takes 4 bogey loads to replenish the bunker. I could manage it with 3 but the incline up into the factory is too steep to push the bogey comfortably if fully laden. And there is no need to rush. This is a part of the shift I like. Once the 4th load is in the bogey I leave it standing and go over to have a smoke with the Nightoutsideman. We exchange nods. I lean my back against the wall on the other side of the hut door from him; sometimes I lower myself down to sit on my heels. Due to the configuration of warehouse and factory buildings there is never any wind here (a very very slight breeze, but only occasionally) and the canal is still, its water black, grey foam spreading out from its banks.

He will have been waiting for me to arrive before making his next cigarette. He used to make one for me but I prefer my own. I strike the match; while I am exhaling on the first draw I flick the match out onto the canal, watching for its smoke but there never is any; if there is I havent been able to see it. He raises his eyebrows, a brief smile. He smiles a lot, speaks very rarely; he just likes to sit there, watching the things that happen. Most of the buildings are unoccupied during the night and their differing shapes and shadows, the shades of black and grey, red-tinged. Now and then he will gesture at the sky, at the bend in the canal, sideways at one of the buildings, to the one where jets of steam suddenly issue from escape pipes, and to high up in the same building, at the large windows where headlike shapes appear frequently. I never quite grasp what he is on about but it probably has to do with plain truths, and I nod, as though acknowledging a contrast. Then when I finish the smoke I flick the dowp out onto the canal, listening for the plop which never comes (which never could come, not in any canal). I wait on a few moments, before going to get the bogey. I like this last push up the incline, that rutted point near the top where the wheels seem to be jamming and the bogey halts and

I cannot hold it any longer! All my

strength's gone! The load's going to roll back down and crash into the canal!

                              and then I grin; I breathe in and shove, continuing on up and through the swing doors into the corridor, still grinning.

I have charge of the boilers. Their bodies are situated in the basement and their mouths range the ground surface area, shut off by solid square hatches with set-in rings. The floor is made of specially treated metal plating so that although it is still very hot it is never too hot such that it is impossible to walk upon when wearing the special boots (metal studded, and perhaps the uppers are of a special substance?). When I arrive with the 4th load of coal I wheel the bogey past the bunker and go straight across to begin stoking. I have a crowbar to insert in the rings to wedge up the hatches which settle at an angle of 100°. With the hatch raised the heat and light from the boiler is tremendous and I have to avert my face while stoking. Asbestos gloves are there to be used but I work without them, simply taking care not to touch the metal parts of the shovel. It is habit now and I cannot remember the last time I burnt my hands. There is an interesting thing that a child would like to see; this is the coaldust dropping from my shovel during the stoking, it ignites simultaneously to touching the floor so that countless tiny fires are always blazing, and it looks startling (diamonds that sparkle). Then I have finished and kick down the hatch, and that thud of impact separating the loud roaring of the open boiler from the dull roaring of the closed boiler that I can never quite anticipate. And I move onto the next. Finally, when I have finished them all, I wheel off the bogey to its position by the bunker then return with the wire-brush to sweep clean the floor of the ground surface. Coalbits will be lying smouldering or burning nearby the hatches; I sweep them straight across and into the water trench next to the basement entrance. Towards the end of the shift I rake out the trench and use what is there on the last stoke. Whenever I forget to do this the trench is full when I come in next evening. The Dayboilerman is responsible. This is his way of remind-ing me not to do it again.

From a distance the entrance to the basement resem-bles another boilermouth but it is set away to the side of the ground surface, and its hatch is permanently raised. There is a step ladder going down, the top of which is welded onto the inside panel of the hatch. I enjoy descending. I grip either side with both hands, sometimes scurrying down to break the existing speed record, other times I go stepping very very slowly, very deliberately, as though engaged upon ultra serious busi-ness to do with submarines or spaceships. I can be stand-ing watching myself from way over beyond the bunker, seeing my head sink from view, vanishing, wondering if it cracked against the edge of the metal plated floor but no, always I just avoid that by the briefest margin possible, gglullp. gone. Then I poke out my head again. Or maybe remain exactly there, just beneath the surface, counting 25 and only then will I reappear, and back down immediately.

*

Nowadays I appreciate no tasks more than those that have me down in the basement. It did use to have its frightening aspects but my imagination was to blame. The black holes is the best example. I would step past them and pretend they were not there, or if they were, that I was not particularly bothered by them. This was daft and I knew it was daft but I was just working out a method of conquering myself. At that time I was having to actually force myself to enter the basement. I would say inwardly; these black holes, they are ordinary black holes, ordinary in the sense that they are man-made, they only exist because of the way the walls have been designed. (They also exist as they do because of the effect the lighting system has on the boilerbodies: permanent shadows.)

The basement is a sealed unit, built to accommodate the boilers; the only entrance/exit is by way of the step ladder. Firstly the boilers were sited then they built the basement, and the rest of the building. It took me a while to understand that fully. And when I had I think I was either over my fear or well on the road to it. It was pretty bad at the time. I had to force myself to sit down beside them, the holes, facing away from them, not able to see them without turning my head. I would sit like that for ages, thinking of horrible things, but not being aware of it till later, sometimes much later, when walking home. One morning the Dayboilerman found me. It was a terrible shock for him. The sound of his boots on the steps of the ladder had reached me but could scarcely correspond to anything I knew so that I wasnt really aware of it beyond my thoughts. Then he was there and his eyes staring as though seeing a ghost, seeming about to collapse with a heart attack. Yet he had been looking for me. I hadnt clocked out at the gate and the timekeeper had asked him to check up. So he was looking for me and when he found me reacted as though I was the last thing he expected to see sitting there. He told people I looked like a zombie. A zombie! But eventually it made me realize he had never managed to conquer himself. He must have been really nervous, terrified about what he *might* find.

The switches for the basement lighting are on the wall behind the ladder so they can be turned on before reaching the bottom, but they are supposed to be kept on permanently. I think the reason for this has to do with the idea of one man being down and then another man coming down without realizing the first is there, and returning back up and switching the lighting off, leaving the first man in total blackness. That would be a horrible thing to happen, particularly to someone new in the job. But I have to admit here and now that I do play about with the switches, sometimes leaving the lighting off during the times I'm away from the basement. I think about how it all looks down there, different things. Also, there is that incredible sensation when switching them back on again later. I go stepping off the ladder with my back to the inner wall, facing away from the shaft of light above, right out into the blackness. Occasionally I will walk 3 or 4 (5 at the most) paces until that feeling of narrowness has me stock-still and trying to reflect on a variety of matters, maybe wondering how it would be having to work in such conditions forever (a miner whose lamp keeps going out?). And I continue standing there, thinking of different things, then slowly but surely I notice I am moving back the way, sensing the approach of that strange feeling of being buried in cotton wool and I am turning to reach for the switches calmly, not panicking at all, getting my bearings from the shaft of light high above at the entrance. And the lighting is immediate throughout the basement, and the noise of everything now audible apparently for the first time, that deep deep humming sound.

The boilerbodies dominate the basement. I can stand watching them. They are large, their shadows rigid but falling on each other (it can seem as though your eyes are blurring). There is a complex of narrow passage-ways between them, just wide enough for a man to walk, carrying a crate of cinders and a rake and shovel perhaps. I used to think a bogey might be adapted to fit the passage-ways but this is not at all necessary; it is possible the idea only occurred to me because of movable objects – I thought it would be good to have one. There are 4 tools: 2 crates plus a rake and a shovel. There are also 2 pairs of boilersuits, 1 for the Day-boilerman and 1 for me; they have to be kept in the basement, if we want to wear boilersuits on the ground surface we have to order different ones for the purpose. I also keep a towel down here which I find necessary. Although the atmosphere is not stifling it must be akin to tropical. I think of equatorial forests full of those peculiar plants, gigantic ones, with brightly coloured buds the size of oranges hanging down the middle, and that constant dripping. But there isnt any dripping in the basement, nothing like that. There is water in the trenches of course, which surrounds the bottom of the boilerbodies. Cinders fall through to here somehow and I rake them out and carry them in a crate to the foot of the ladder, dumping them into the other crate which I will carry up later on, for eventual use in the last stoke. I enjoy carrying the crate between the boilerbodies. I take different routes and go quickly or slowly, sometimes very very slowly, studying my boots as they land at that point on the passageway nearest to the trench. Even though I work naked I continue to wear the boots. I once tried it barefoot but the edges of the trenches get quite slippy when I'm raking the cinders out; also a daft thing, I was being continually tempted into the water, just to dip my feet (but if I had succumbed to that I would maybe have gone in for a swim!).

The trenches are narrow and they slope in below the bottoms of the boilerbodies so that cinders can become stuck, and stuck fast, there seems to be a great many crannies. I know most of them through having used the rake so often. This part of the job is good, the raking noise and my own silence, that clung of the rakehead below the surface of the water on the sides of the trench, the scraping noise of its teeth in the crannies. I could have expected both that and the sense of touch to grate on me but they dont, perhaps because they come from outside of me altogether. I work silently, and in silence. It is an important point. The idea of the work noise is funny, how it would appear to somebody (not the Dayboilerman) poking his head down the ladder, seeing how all the objects and everything are so stationary, just taking it for granted for a spell while not being conscious of anything else, not until that moment he has become aware of something, of an unexpected noise, rhythmic, and I couldnt be seen from there because of the shapes and shadows, only the clung and scraping sound; after a moment the person would react by snorting, maybe giving himself a telling off for being so daft, and then he would climb back up and out as quickly as he could, trying to kid on he wasnt bothered by it.

But nobody from outside ever comes down into the basement. Firstly the ground surface area needs to be crossed and it cannot be crossed without special footwear. If anybody wishes to attract my attention they either shout or batter the floor with a crowbar. It happens only rarely and I seldom respond since it is always to advise me that the pressure isnt being maintained. This I discover myself sooner or later because of the safety precautions. I might be wrong not to respond. I sometimes wonder whether to ask the Dayboilerman what he does. But his perception of the job will differ radically from my own. It cannot be avoided, he is on constant day and I am on constant night, we each have our own distractions. Yes, I can still be distracted; in some ways it is essential to the work; but I cannot be distracted against my wishes. If I think of things they must be things I wish to think of.

*

I used to make myself sit by the black hole farthest from the entrance; it lies on the same side but to reach it I have to walk to the wall opposite the ladder then follow the passageway there, right around and into the corner. I would bring the boilersuit to sit on and the towel to lean my back on against the wall; then I lit a cigarette. Smoking is frowned upon down here but I've always done it; I really enjoy it, finishing a particular part of the work and sitting down quietly and lighting one. Sometimes when I sit down I leave the cigarettes and matches beside me for a while before smoking; other times I'm smoking even before sitting down. One thing I used to do in the early days, I used to push the matches and cigarettes inside the hole. I sat there for a long period afterwards, till finally I knelt and withdrew them without looking in, just using my hand to feel around.

There is nothing extraordinary about these black holes, they are cavities and short tunnels. I found them of interest because they had never been seen into since the factory's original construction. I still find the idea quite interesting. When I first found them I thought they were just inshots, little gaps, and I sat by them not bothering. Then one night after sitting a while I suddenly was kneeling down and peering in and I couldnt see anything, nothing at all. I struck a match and the light scarcely penetrated. It was really funny. Then I had to push in my hand; I discovered the wall, and then a tunnel veering off at a tangent. I could have brought in a torch or a candle, and a mirror maybe, but

I never did. If I remember correctly I was wanting to check the dimensions of the wall in relation to it, the cavity and tunnel. I knew it had to be some sort of double wall, but probably a triple one, as part of the safety precautions. I went round by the canal pathway to look at the outside of the building but that told me nothing. On this particular side of the factory the pathway only goes along a few yards before narrowing and tapering out altogether, with the wall going straight down into the water.

There were quite a lot of things about it that bothered me at the time but nowadays it all seems hazy. But I think the main factor must connect to the idea of isolation, maybe bringing on a form of deprivation or something. It wasnt good when I had to sit by the black holes at first, some of my imaginings were horrible. I just had to stick it out and conquer myself. I had to succeed and I did succeed. It taught me a lot about myself and has given me confidence. Sometimes I feel a bit smug, as if I've reached a higher level than the others in the factory; but I dont speak to many of them, I just get on and do the job, enjoying its various aspects.

The Place!

Deep water. I want to float through breakers and over breastroking across uplifted by them. This is what I need. And upon the deep open sea. Freshwater wont do. Where are the breakers in freshwater. None. You dont fucking get them. I want to be by a sheer rockface. The steep descent to reach the sea where at hightide the caves are inaccessible by foot alone. I have to startle birds in their nests from within the caves. At hightide the rockplunge into the deep. That is what I want. That. I can swim fine and I can swim fine at my own pace and I have no illusions about my prowess. I'm not getting fucked about any longer.

There is a place I know on the coast. I cant go there. It is not in reach. The remains of a Druid cemetery close by, accounts for a few tourists. The tourists never visit the Place. Maybe they do. But it isnt a real reason for not going. There are real reasons, real reasons. My christ what a find this place was. I climbed down a dangerous part of the rockface. Right down and disregarding mostly all I know of climbing down the dangerous parts. Only perhaps 25 feet. The tide was in. I wanted to fall in. I wanted to dive in. I did not know if it was safe to dive in. If there were rocks jutting beneath the surface. So I did not want to dive in. I wanted to fall in and find out whether it was safe for diving. But if I fell onto submerged rocks I might have been killed so I did not want to fall in at all for fuck sake which is why I clung at shallow clumps of weed-grass, loose slate; and it was holding fast, supporting me, the weight. I kept getting glimpses of the caves. Impossible to reach at hightide unless by swimming. When I got down to where I could only go I saw the rocks in the depth and had to get away at that moment seeing the rocks there I had to getaway at once and each grain of matter was now loosening on my touch my toes cramped and I had to cling on this loose stuff applying no none absolutely no pressure at all but, just balancing there with the toes cramped in this slight crevice.

An Enquiry Concerning
Human Understanding

During a time prior to this a major portion of my
energy was devoted to recollection. These recollections
were to be allowed to surface only for my material
benefit. Each item dredged was to have been noted as
the lesson learned so that never again would I find
myself in the situation effected through said item. A
nerve wracking affair. And I lacked the discipline. Yet
I knew all the items so well there seemed little point
in dredging them up just to remember them when I in
fact knew them so well already. It was desirable to take
it along in calm, stately fashion; rationalizing like the
reasonable being. This would have been the thing. This
would have been for the experience. And I devoted real
time to past acts with a view to an active future. The
first major item dredged was an horse by the name of
Bronze Arrow which fell at the Last in a novice hurdle
race at Wincanton for maidens at starting. I had this
thing to Eighty Quid at the remunerative odds of eleven-
double-one-to-two against. Approaching the Last *Bronze
Arrow* is steadily increasing his lead to Fifteen Lengths
. . . Fallen at the Last number two *Bronze Arrow*. This
type of occurrence is most perplexing. One scarcely

conceives of the ideal method of tackling such an item. But: regarding Description; the best Description of such an item is Ach, Fuck that for a Game.

POCKET PENGUINS

POCKET PENGUINS